The Calvin and Hobbes
LAZY SUNDAY BOOK

A Collection of Sunday Calvin and Hobbes Cartoons
by BILL WATTERSON

SCHOLASTIC INC.

New York Toronto London Auckland Sydney

To Rich West

ISBN 0-590-10678-3

12 11 10 9 8 7 6 5 4 3 2 1   7 8 9/9 0 1 2/0

Printed in the U.S.A.   14

First Scholastic printing, September 1997

HMPH.

YES! THE INCREDIBLE SPACEMAN SPIFF SURVIVES! DAZED, BUT UNHURT, OUR HERO CRAWLS FROM THE SMOLDERING WRECKAGE!

SPIFF SETS OFF ACROSS THE PLANET SURFACE. AN OMINOUS, SHADOWY FIGURE FLITS ACROSS A NEARBY HILLTOP! AN ALIEN!

OUR HERO DARTS BEHIND A ROCK AND SETS HIS ZORCHER ON "SHAKE AND BAKE." THE ALIEN APPROACHES!

HI CALVIN! I SEE YOU, SO YOU CAN STOP HIDING NOW! ARE YOU PLAYING COWBOYS OR SOMETHING? CAN I PLAY TOO?

ZOUNDS! THE BOOGER BEING IS IN ALLIANCE WITH THE NAGGON MOTHER SHIP THAT SHOT SPIFF DOWN IN THE FIRST PLACE! OUR HERO OPTS FOR A SPEEDY GETAWAY!

Calvin and Hobbes by WATTERSON

"BEFORE BEGINNING ANY HOME-PLUMBING REPAIR, MAKE SURE YOU POSSESS THE PROPER TOOLS FOR THE JOB."

"CHECK THE FOLLOWING LIST OF HANDY EXPLETIVES, AND SEE THAT YOU KNOW HOW TO USE THEM."

CALVIN WAKES UP ONE MORNING TO FIND HE NO LONGER EXISTS IN THE THIRD DIMENSION! HE IS **2-D**!

THINNER THAN A SHEET OF PAPER, CALVIN HAS NO SURFACE AREA ON THE BOTTOM OF HIS FEET! HE IS IMMOBILE!

ONLY BY "WAVING" HIS BODY CAN CALVIN CREATE ENOUGH FRICTION WITH THE GROUND TO MOVE!

HAVING WIDTH BUT NO THICKNESS, CALVIN IS VULNERABLE TO THE SLIGHTEST GUST OF WIND!

TO AVOID DRAFTS, HE TWISTS HIMSELF INTO A TUBE, AND ROLLS ACROSS THE FLOOR!

SOMEONE IS COMING! CALVIN QUICKLY STANDS UP STRAIGHT.

TURNING PERFECTLY SIDEWAYS, HE IS A NEARLY INVISIBLE VERTICAL LINE! NO ONE WILL NOTICE!

HEY DAD, KNOW WHY YOU DIDN'T SEE ME ALL MORNING?? I WAS TWO-DIMENSIONAL!

HMMM, I'LL BET YOU CAN'T DO IT ALL AFTERNOON, TOO...

DEAR!

Calvin and Hobbes by WATTERSON

OY OH BOY OH BOY OH BOY OH BOY OH BOY OH BOY OH BOY OH BOY OH BOY

WAIT! WAIT! I'VE GOT TO SAVOR THIS MOMENT! THE BRILLIANCE OF IT ALL! I'M A GENIUS! A SHEER *GENIUS!*

SUSIE'S PLAYING ON THE SIDEWALK! NOW'S MY CHANCE TO USE THE SNOWBALL I'VE BEEN SAVING IN THE FREEZER!

SHE'LL NEVER EXPECT A SNOWBALL IN *JUNE!* BOY, WILL SHE BE MAD! HA HA HA!

THIS IS GOING TO BE GREAT! HERE IT COMES! OH BOY! OH BOY!

HEY SUSIE!!

PIFF

I *MISSED!* DARN IT DARN IT DARN IT!! OF ALL THE MISERABLE LUCK!

AAARRGHH!

THERE MUST'VE BEEN A CROSS BREEZE! I CAN'T BELIEVE IT! I SAVED THAT SNOWBALL FOR THREE WHOLE MONTHS! I...

SCOOP SCOOP

I.. I...UH...

POW

THE IRONY OF THIS IS JUST SICKENING.

THE DREADED SCUM BEINGS FIRE! SPACEMAN SPIFF IS *HIT!*

IT NEVER FAILS. I JUST WASHED AND WAXED THIS THING.

OUR HERO, THE INTREPID SPACEMAN SPIFF, STRUGGLES WITH THE CONTROLS OF HIS DAMAGED SPACECRAFT!

THE FREEM PROPULSION BLASTERS ARE USELESS! SPIFF CRASHES ONTO THE SURFACE OF AN ALIEN PLANET!

UNSCATHED, THE FEARLESS SPACE EXPLORER EMERGES FROM THE SMOLDERING WRECKAGE! HE IS MAROONED ON A HOSTILE WORLD!

SCORCHED BY TWIN SUNS, THE PLANET IS NOTHING BUT BARREN ROCK AND METHANE! THERE'S NO HOPE OF FINDING FOOD OR WATER!

SPIFF COLLAPSES! OH NO, A HIDEOUS ALIEN SPOTS HIM! IN HIS WEAKENED STATE, SPIFF IS NO MATCH FOR THE MONSTER! *THIS COULD BE THE END!!*

LUNCHTIME! I BROUGHT YOU A SANDWICH AND SOME LEMONADE.

BRING THE DISHES BACK WHEN YOU'RE DONE, OK?

...OH WELL.

THANKS, MOM.

Calvin and Hobbes by WATTERSON

AH·CHOO!

WHEN ... NO BRAINS.

AH.. AH.. AH.. **AH**

CHOOO!!

THE FORCE OF THE NASAL EXPLOSION SENDS CALVIN REELING THROUGH THE STRATOSPHERE!

WITH LESS AND LESS AIR TO RESIST HIS MOMENTUM, HE BREAKS THE PULL OF EARTH'S GRAVITY AND HURLS PAST THE MOON!

AS HE PASSES OUT OF THE GALAXY, CALVIN REFLECTS ON THE WISDOM OF COVERING ONE'S MOUTH WHEN SNEEZING TO DEFLECT THE PROPULSION.

ALAS, IT IS KNOWLEDGE GAINED TOO LATE FOR POOR CALVIN, THE HUMAN SATELLITE! ...BUT WAIT! ANOTHER SNEEZE IS BREWING! CALVIN TURNS HIMSELF AROUND!

THE SECOND SNEEZE ROCKETS HIM BACK TO EARTH! HE'S SAVED! IT'S A MIRACLE!

AH CHOO!

GOD BLESS YOU.

OH, HE *DOES*, MOM. HE *DOES*.

WATTERSON

Calvin and Hobbes
by WATTERSON

Calvin and Hobbes

by WATTERSON

 WIPE THAT GRIN OFF YOUR FACE!

 WELL, HOBBES, HOW DO I LOOK?

I'M DOING MY BEST TO BITE MY TONGUE.

 I CUT OUT CONSTRUCTION PAPER FEATHERS AND TAPED THEM ON MY ARMS SO I CAN FLY! PRETTY NEAT, HUH?

 IF PAPER FEATHERS ARE ALL IT TAKES TO FLY, DON'T YOU THINK WE'D HAVE HEARD ABOUT IT BEFORE?

IT TAKES AN UNCOMMON MIND TO THINK OF THESE THINGS, HOBBES.

 I'D AGREE WITH THAT.

HERE'S A GORGE. THIS IS A GOOD SPOT.

 YOU'RE GOING TO JUMP OFF THIS LEDGE?

HECK NO! I NEED MOMENTUM! I WANT YOU TO TOSS ME OVER.

 YOU UNDERSTAND I ASSUME NO RESPONSIBILITY FOR THIS?

RIGHT. I GET THE PATENT.

 HEAVE!

I'M FLYING! I'M FLYING!

 I'M..... UH OH... I

 DON'T SELL THE BIKE SHOP, ORVILLE.

SHUT UP AND GO GET ME SOME ANTISEPTIC.

32

34

A DAZED SPACEMAN SPIFF CRAWLS FROM THE SMOKING WRECKAGE OF HIS SHIP!

OUR HERO NOW REGRETS NOT BUYING A TOWING RIDER ON HIS INSURANCE POLICY.

THE COURAGEOUS SPACEMAN SPIFF HAS BEEN CAPTURED BY THE HIDEOUS ZORGS OF PLANET X-13!

LED THROUGH THE DANK CORRIDORS OF THE DUNGEON, SPIFF LOOKS IN VAIN FOR AN OPPORTUNITY TO ESCAPE!

OUR HERO IS BROUGHT BEFORE THE ZORG DESPOT!

SO *THIS* IS THE FAMED SPACE EXPLORER SPIFF! I'VE WAITED A LONG TIME FOR THIS MOMENT, EARTHLING SCUM!

YOU HAVE KNOWLEDGE WE NEED. COOPERATE, AND WE'LL KILL YOU RATHER PAINLESSLY.

LET'S DISPENSE WITH THE PLEASANTRIES, YOU TWISTED SPACE CRUSTACEAN. WHAT IS IT YOU WANT FROM ME?

A SUMMARY OF LEWIS AND CLARK'S EXPEDITION TO THE PACIFIC!

HA! WILD ZONTARS COULDN'T DRAG THAT INFORMATION OUT OF ME! DO YOUR WORST!

YOU DIDN'T READ THE ASSIGNMENT, DID YOU, CALVIN?

CALVIN and HOBBES
by WATTERSON

ZZ-ZZZZ

BBWAAAHH

CALVIN, IT'S TIME TO WAKE UP.

Z

CALVIN, IT'S TIME TO WAKE UP.

C'MON, YOU'LL BE LATE FOR SCHOOL.

Z

MY DREAMS ARE GETTING WAY TOO LITERAL.

CALViN and HObbES

by WATERSON

First there was nothing...

...then there was Calvin!

Calvin, the mighty god, creates the universe with pure will!

From utter nothingness comes swirling form! Life begins where once was void!

But Calvin is no kind and loving god! He's one of the old gods! He demands sacrifice!

Yes, Calvin is a god of the underworld! And the puny inhabitants of earth displease him!

The great Calvin ignores their pleas for mercy and the doomed writhe in agony!

HAVE YOU SEEN HOW ABSORBED CALVIN IS WITH THOSE TINKERTOYS? HE'S CREATING WHOLE WORLDS OVER THERE!

I'LL BET HE GROWS UP TO BE AN ARCHITECT.

WATERSON

CALVIN and HOBBES

by WATTERSON

YAWN

PUTT PUTT PUTT PUTT PUTT PUTT

Z

SCRITCH SCRATCH

ZZ
MMM..

RUB RUB RUB

ZZ
..RRRR..

SHOOF SHOOF SHOOF

ZZ
..OOO..MM..

ITCH ITCH ITCH ITCH

ZZ
YOW WOW
YOW WOW
ZZ..

NKG
K
ZZ..

HMMMMM

ZZZ
Z

THAT SIGH OUGHT TO GET ME OUT OF A FEW YEARS' PURGATORY.

Z

43

Calvin and Hobbes

by WATTERSON

"HERE'S A BOX OF CRAYONS. I NEED SOME ILLUSTRATIONS FOR A STORY I'M WRITING."

"YOU CAN DRAW SOMETHING BESIDES TIGERS, CAN'T YOU?"

"SURE. LEOPARDS, PUMAS, OCELOTS.. ..YOU NAME IT."

"HERE, DAD, READ *THIS* STORY TONIGHT. I WROTE IT AND HOBBES ILLUSTRATED IT."

"..UM... OK."

"THE DAD WHO LIVED TO REGRET BEING MEAN TO HIS KID."

"WHAT ARE YOU PAUSING FOR? KEEP READING."

Barney's dad was really bad,
So Barney hatched a plan.
When his dad said, "Eat your peas!"
Barney shouted, "NO!" and ran.

peas

Barney

Barney tricked his mean ol' dad,
And locked him in the cellar,
His mom never found out
    where he'd gone,
'Cause Barney didn't tell her.

door   key

There his dad spent his life,
Eating mice and gruel.
With every bite for fifty years
He was sorry he'd been cruel.
    THE END.

mice

Barney's dad

"YOU KNOW HOW A LOT OF STORIES HAVE MORALS TO THEM...?"

"I *GET* IT, I *GET* IT!"

WATTERSON & HOBS

DID YOU MAKE ANY RESOLUTIONS FOR THE NEW YEAR?

HECK NO.

I'M FINE JUST THE WAY I AM! WHY SHOULD *I* CHANGE?

IN FACT, I THINK IT'S HIGH TIME THE WORLD STARTED CHANGING TO SUIT *ME*! I DON'T SEE WHY *I* SHOULD DO ALL THE CHANGING AROUND HERE!

IF THE NEW YEAR REQUIRES RESOLUTIONS, I SAY IT'S UP TO EVERYONE ELSE, NOT ME! *I* DON'T NEED TO IMPROVE! EVERYONE *ELSE* DOES!

HOW ABOUT YOU? DID YOU MAKE ANY RESOLUTIONS.?

WELL, I HAD RESOLVED TO BE LESS OFFENDED BY HUMAN NATURE, BUT I THINK I BLEW IT ALREADY.

CALVIN and HOBBES by WATTERSON

TWO PARTS SLUSH...
ONE PART SOLID ICE...
ONE PART HARD-PACKED SNOW...
A DASH OF ASSORTED DEBRIS...

SCULPT INTO SPHERE, AND SERVE AT HIGH VELOCITY WITHOUT WARNING.

OH, BOY, HERE COMES SUSIE!

HEY, SUSIE!

WHAP!

HA HA! I GOTCHA, YOU DUMB GIRL!!

AUGHH! MY EYEBALL! WHERE'S MY EYEBALL?!

WHAT ARE YOU TALKING ABOUT? I HIT YOU IN THE BACK.

IT KNOCKED MY EYEBALL OUT! FIND IT AND PACK IT IN SNOW SO THEY CAN SAVE IT! OW! OW!

GOSH, DID YOU REALLY LOSE YOUR EYEBALL? I DIDN'T KNOW THEY CAME OUT! WOW. I'M REALLY SORRY. I DIDN'T MEAN TO KNOCK IT OUT. CAN I SEE THE SOCKET? BOY, WHERE DO YOU SUPPOSE IT ROLLED?

SOMEWHERE OVER THERE, POOP HEAD!!

BOOT

WATTERSON

WHAT ARE YOU DOING?

MY EYEBALL FELL OUT. HELP ME LOOK FOR IT.

CALVIN AND HOBBES by WATTERSON

PLANET BOG — POOLS OF TOXIC CHEMICALS BUBBLE UNDER A CHOKING ATMOSPHERE OF POISONOUS GASES.

...BUT ASIDE FROM THAT, IT'S NOT MUCH LIKE EARTH.

WE FIND SPACEMAN SPIFF STRUGGLING ACROSS THE TERRAIN OF A DISTANT PLANET!

SUDDENLY THE GROUND BEGINS TO SHAKE! A CLOUD OF DUST APPEARS ON THE HORIZON! IT'S A ZORG!!

OUR HERO RUNS FOR COVER, BUT THE ZORG IS INSTANTLY UPON HIM!

SPIFF FIRES HIS BLASTER, BUT THE WEAPON IS USELESS AGAINST THE MONSTER!

THE FEARLESS SPACE EXPLORER IS TAKEN TO THE ZORG'S CAVE, WHERE HE DISCOVERS A VAT OF BOILING WATER! OH NO! OUR HERO IS ABOUT TO BE COOKED ALIVE!

SPIFF'S MIND RACES FURIOUSLY...

WELL? GET IN.

DON'T YOU WANT TO LEAN WAY, WAY OVER, AND TEST HOW HOT THE WATER IS?

CALVIN and HOBBES
by WATTERSON

IT'S FREEZING UPSTAIRS!

CAN I TAKE SOME LOGS UP TO MY ROOM?

HEY, YOU'RE ON MY SIDE OF THE BED.

THESE SHEETS ARE FREEZING!

YEAH, WELL... AAUGHH! YOUR FEET ARE LIKE ICE! GET AWAY FROM ME!

BUT MY SIDE'S ALL COLD!

WELL DON'T GET ME COLD! MOVE OVER!

SURE, YOU'VE GOT A FUR COAT! I'M JUST WEARING PAJAMAS.

QUIT PULLING THE BLANKETS, WILLYA?

I HARDLY HAVE ANY, YOU HOG! GIMME THOSE!

YOU'RE LETTING IN COLD AIR! QUIT IT! QUIT IT!

SERVES YOU RIGHT, MR. MOSTY-TOASTY! SEE WHAT IT'S LIKE BEING COLD!

YAHHHH!!

EAT FEATHERS, FUZZ BALL!

WHAP OOF ZPOW

MOVE OVER. YOU'RE GETTING MY SIDE ALL HOT.

OPEN THE WINDOW. I'M ROASTING.

CALVIN and HOBBES

THE LATE CRETACEOUS PERIOD... WHEN DINOSAURS RULED THE EARTH!

by WATTERSON

..AND CALVIN RULED THE DINOSAURS!

THE TERRIBLE TYRANNOSAURUS SINKS ITS TEETH INTO A TRICERATOPS!

TRIUMPHANT AGAIN, THE UNDISPUTED KING OF DINOSAURS LETS OUT A MIGHTY ROAR!

WITH SAVAGE FEROCITY, THE MONSTER BEGINS ITS FEAST! LIMB-SEVERING, BONE-CRUNCHING AND TENDON-SNAPPING, HE...

CALVIN! THAT'S DISGUSTING!

FOR HEAVEN'S SAKE, SLOW DOWN AND CHEW QUIETLY!

THE TERRIBLE TYRANNOSAURUS RESUMES EATING, MORTIFIED THAT SOMEONE MIGHT SEE HIM.

56

CALVIN and HOBBES
by WATTERSON

YOU JUST HAD ONE.

WILL YOU GET ME A GLASS OF WATER?

I WANT ONE TO KEEP BY THE BED, SO I CAN DOUSE THIS GUY IF HE STARTS SNORING.

GOOD NIGHT, CALVIN.

Z

HEE HEE HEE HEE

OH, GREAT. HE'S DREAMING AGAIN.

SNIFF SNIFF SNIFF

WHERE DO YOU THINK YOU ARE, YOU IMBECILE? OUT IN THE JUNGLE?

...MM... HEH HEH HEH

IF HE STARTS "RUNNING," HE'S GONNA GET A PILLOW IN THE KISSER.

SNIFF SNIFF

HEY! WHERE ARE YOU GOING ??

SOMNAMBULISTS GIVE ME THE CREEPS. WHY ARE WE GOING TO THE KITCHEN?

Z

CALVIN! WHAT ARE YOU DOING? HAVE YOU BEEN SLEEPWALKING ??

I WAS COMPLETELY AWAKE! IT'S THIS DOPE WHO'S SLEEPWALKING! I JUST FOLLOWED HIM.

I PUT HIM BACK TO BED. HE COULDN'T GIVE ANY REASON FOR BEING UP.

DO YOU SUPPOSE IT MEANS ANYTHING? LOOK, HE GOT OUT ALL THE TUNA!

Calvin and Hobbes by WATTERSON

I CALL THIS "LOOKOUT" HILL.

YES, YOU CAN CERTAINLY SEE FAR FROM UP HERE.

I CALL IT "LOOKOUT" HILL BECAUSE THAT'S WHAT YOU YELL WHENEVER WE GO DOWN IT.

YOU KNOW, SOMETIMES IT SEEMS THINGS GO BY TOO QUICKLY.

WE'RE SO BUSY WATCHING OUT FOR WHAT'S JUST AHEAD OF US THAT WE DON'T TAKE THE TIME TO ENJOY WHERE WE ARE.

DAYS GO BY AND WE HARDLY NOTICE THEM. LIFE BECOMES A BLUR.

OFTEN IT TAKES SOME CALAMITY TO MAKE US LIVE IN THE PRESENT.

THEN SUDDENLY WE WAKE UP AND SEE ALL THE MISTAKES WE'VE MADE, BUT IT'S TOO LATE TO CHANGE ANYTHING.

IT'S LIKE... ...IT'S LIKE...

IT'S LIKE WHAT?

IT'S LIKE *SOME*THING... I JUST CAN'T THINK OF IT.

CALVIN AND HOBBES by WATTERSON

A VOICE CACKLES IN CALVIN'S RADIO. "ENEMY FIGHTERS AT TWO O'CLOCK!"

ROGER. WHAT SHOULD I DO UNTIL THEN?

CALVIN'S F-4 PHANTOM SCREAMS ACROSS THE SKY!

BUT WHAT'S THIS? THE CANOPY GLASS IS ALL SMEARED! HE CAN HARDLY SEE THROUGH IT!

OH, NO! THE THROTTLE SNAPS OFF IN HIS HAND!

CALVIN'S ONLY HOPE IS TO LAND, BUT THE WHEELS REFUSE TO OPEN! THEY'RE STUCK!

FRANTICALLY CALVIN TRIES TO EJECT, BUT THE COCKPIT IS FUSED TOGETHER! HIS JET IS A HOPELESS MESS! EVERYTHING IS GOING WRONG!

STUPID MODEL.

Calvin and Hobbes
by WATTERSON

C'MON, HOBBES. LET ME UP INTO THE TREE FORT.

SAY THE PASSWORD.

NO! YOU KNOW IT'S ME! LET ME UP!

YOU MAY BE SOME OTHER KID IN DISGUISE.

IT'S *ME*, CALVIN! LET ME UP, YOU HAIRBALL BARFER!

AN INSULT! WELL, YOU CAN JUST STAY DOWN THERE *FOREVER*, MR. STINKER.

OH, NO! HERE COMES SUSIE! LET ME UP QUICK, SO WE CAN THROW THINGS AT HER! HURRY! LET DOWN THE ROPE!

LA DE DA DUM DOO ♪ ♫

SHE'S COMING! QUICK! LET DOWN THE ROPE! I'M SORRY I INSULTED YOU! OK? SEE, I SAID I WAS SORRY! CAN'T YOU LET DOWN THE ROPE?!

YOU HAVE TO SAY THE PASSWORD.

..*Verse Seven:* TIGERS ARE PERFECT, THE *E*-PIT-O-ME OF GOOD LOOKS AND GRACE AND QUIET..UH..UM..DIGNITY..

I WAS GOING TO ASK YOU TO COME OVER AND PLAY HOUSE, BUT I THINK YOU'D BE A WEIRD EXAMPLE FOR OUR CHILDREN.

ONE OF THESE DAYS I'M GOING TO MAKE YOU INTO A RUG! YOU HEAR ME?? A RUG!

Calvin and Hobbes

by WATTERSON

THE CALL GOES OUT! WE'RE ON THE MOVE!

UP THROUGH THE WINDING MAZE! FASTER! FASTER!

CALVIN SCRAMBLES UP THE GRAINY TUNNEL!

OUT HE POPS INTO THE BLINDING SUN! CALVIN THE ANT RUSHES DOWN THE HILL TO THE BRICK WALK!

OTHER ANTS RUSH AROUND HIM IN THEIR MAD HURRY! CALVIN TRIES TO KEEP UP!

AT LAST HE REACHES THE MONSTROUS DEAD CATERPILLAR! WITHOUT PAUSING, HE HOISTS IT UP!

THE QUEEN DEMANDS HIS TIRELESS TOIL! CALVIN IS BACK OFF TO THE ANT-HILL AS FAST AS HE CAN GO!

WORK, WORK, WORK! THAT'S ALL I'M GOOD FOR AROUND HERE!

I HARDLY THINK PICKING UP YOUR ROOM ONCE IN A WHILE QUALIFIES YOU AS A SLAVE.

CALVIN and HOBBES by WATTERSON

THIS IS CALVIN, YOUR CAPTAIN, SPEAKING...

...JUST TO REASSURE YOU THAT, YES, THERE IS SOMEONE UP FRONT.

CALVIN PILOTS THE JET AIRLINER ACROSS THE COUNTRY AT 35,000 FEET.

HE IS GIVEN CLEARANCE TO LAND. BUT WHAT'S THIS? A PLANE FROM A RIVAL AIRLINE IS MAKING FOR THE SAME RUNWAY TO SHAVE PRECIOUS MINUTES OFF ITS SCHEDULE!

IT'S A 600-MPH GAME OF CHICKEN! CALVIN PULLS BACK ON THE THROTTLE AND LURCHES AHEAD!

THE OTHER PILOT TRIES TO CUT CALVIN OFF WITH A SUDDEN DROP IN ALTITUDE!

CALVIN SWITCHES ON THE "FASTEN SEAT BELT" LIGHT IN THE CABIN, AND DOES A BARREL ROLL!

AT 5 Gs, CALVIN HOPES NOT TO BLACK OUT!

AS THEY CLOSE IN ON THE RUNWAY, THE OTHER PILOT HAS NO CHOICE BUT TO PULL UP AND CIRCLE AROUND AGAIN! CALVIN WINS!

HEY, MOM, IS IT TRUE I COULD GET A PILOT'S LICENSE AT AGE 14?

NO.

CALVIN and HOBBES by WATTERSON

ZZZZZZZZZZZZZZZ

FILTH! CONTAMINATION! PESTILENCE! HA HA HA!

OF ALL LIVING CREATURES, FEW ARE MORE REPULSIVE THAN CALVIN THE BUG!

HE EXISTS ONLY TO SUCK BLOOD AND TRANSMIT PARASITIC DISEASE!

SEARCHING FOR SOMEONE TO INFECT, CALVIN FLIES LOW OVER THE PICNIC TABLE!

INGREDIENTS: SALT,

HIS SENSITIVE ANTENNAE PICK UP THE SCENT OF HUMAN FLESH!

TOUCHING DOWN, CALVIN INSERTS HIS NEEDLELIKE PROBOSCIS INTO A VEIN! PROTOZOANS IN HIS SALIVA QUICKLY INDUCE PLAGUE!

WILL YOU STOP THAT AWFUL SLURPING?! YOU'RE MAKING ME SICK!

FWOOOOSH

AS IF LIFE ISN'T SHORT ENOUGH.

CALVIN and HOBBES by WATTERSON

SPACEMAN SPIFF EXPLORES THE OUTERMOST REACHES OF THE UNIVERSE.

BY POPULAR REQUEST.

INTREPID EXPLORER SPACEMAN SPIFF LANDS ON AN UNCHARTED PLANET. WHAT STRANGE WONDERS WILL HE DISCOVER HERE?

SPIFF SETS OUT IN SEARCH OF SENTIENT LIFE!

WHAT A STRANGE PLANET THIS IS! ITS SURFACE IS SURPRISINGLY SOFT AND POROUS!

AND HERE CURIOUS GEYSERS BLAST HOT AIR!

SUDDENLY IT DAWNS ON HIM! SPIFF IS NOT ON THE PLANET'S SURFACE AT ALL! HE'S WALKING ON A RECLINING ALIEN!!

OUR HERO SETS HIS DEATH RAY BLASTER.

ZZ.. MMF HM?

I GOT A HIT!

SAFE!

OK, THAT WAS A SINGLE. I HAVE A GHOST RUNNER HERE NOW, SO I CAN BAT AGAIN.

AND MY GHOST RUNNERS WHO *WERE* ON FIRST AND SECOND BASE ARE NOW ON SECOND AND THIRD, RIGHT?

NOPE. THEY'RE BOTH OUT.

OUT?!

MY GHOST OUTFIELDER TAGGED YOUR GHOST GOING TO THIRD, AND THREW TO MY GHOST SECOND BASEMAN. IT WAS A BRILLIANT DOUBLE PLAY.

THAT NEVER HAPPENED!

YOU'VE GOT TWO OUTS.

WELL, MY GHOST ON FIRST JUST STOLE HOME, SO I'VE GOT ANOTHER RUN! HA HA, SMARTY!

YEAH, WELL, ALL MY OUTFIELD GHOSTS JUST RAN IN AND BEAT THE TOBACCO JUICE OUT OF HIM.

HA! THE GHOST UMPIRE JUST SUSPENDED ALL YOUR GHOSTS FOR ETERNITY. THEY'RE OUT OF THE GAME.

HMPH! IF MY GHOSTS DON'T PLAY, *I* DON'T PLAY.

YOU FORFEIT THE GAME THEN! YOU LOSE AUTOMATICALLY IF YOU QUIT!

THE GHOST CROWD SUPPORTS ME. THEY'RE "BOO"-ING YOU!

SOMETIMES I WISH I LIVED IN A NEIGHBORHOOD WITH MORE KIDS.

Calvin and Hobbes

by WATTERSON

CALVIN and HOBBES by WATTERSON

DINOSAURS EVERYWHERE FLEE FOR THEIR LIVES!

CALVIN IS COMING!

THE LATE CRETACEOUS: THE LAST EPOCH OF THE MIGHTY DINOSAURS!

KING OF THE THUNDER LIZARDS IS THE FEARSOME CALVIN, THE TYRANNOSAURUS!

SEVEN TONS OF MUSCLE AND TEETH. HE SEARCHES FOR PREY!

CALVIN, FOR GOODNESS' SAKE, STOP STOMPING AROUND! YOU'RE DRIVING ME CRAZY!

OW!! CHOMP!

HOW DID THE FEARSOME TYRANNOSAURUS BECOME EXTINCT? NOW WE KNOW!

Calvin and Hobbes

by WATTERSON

SCHOOL'S OUT! FREE AT LAST!

AND JUST SIX PRECIOUS HOURS BEFORE BED TO FORGET EVERYTHING I LEARNED TODAY.

I HATE COMING HOME FROM SCHOOL. I NEVER KNOW IF HOBBES IS WAITING TO POUNCE ON ME.

MAYBE I CAN STAND OFF TO THE SIDE HERE, AND PUSH THE DOOR OPEN WITH A STICK.

I'M HOME!

WHAT DO YOU DO, WAIT UNTIL YOU SEE THE WHITES OF MY EYES?!?

BOY, YOU SHOULD'VE *SEEN* THEM! THEY WERE AS BIG AS DINNER PLATES! HOO HOO HOO!

Calvin and Hobbes

by WATTERSON

UH-OH.

SOMETHING IS VERY WRONG HERE.

CALVIN HAS MYSTERIOUSLY SHRUNK TO A QUARTER OF AN INCH TALL!

HOW CAN HE MAKE HIS PLIGHT KNOWN TO HIS PARENTS WHEN HE'S SMALLER THAN A PENNY?

CALVIN GETS AN IDEA! HE GRABS THE LEG OF OF A PASSING HOUSEFLY AND FLIES TO HIS DAD'S CAMERA!

ONCE THERE, HE CLIMBS UP AND SETS THE SELF-TIMER.

JUMPING ON THE SHUTTER, CALVIN HAS FIFTEEN SHORT SECONDS TO GET IN FRONT OF THE LENS!

WITH LUCK, CALVIN'S DAD WILL HAVE THE FILM DEVELOPED SOON, AND DISCOVER WHAT HAS HAPPENED!

WHAT HAPPENED?! LOOK AT ALL THESE TERRIBLE PICTURES! I DON'T REMEMBER TAKING THESE. WHO'S THAT LITTLE SPECK IN THE DISTANCE ALL THE TIME? YOU HAVEN'T BEEN FOOLING WITH MY CAMERA, HAVE YOU?

ME? HECK, NO. MAYBE YOU SHOULD GET THE CAMERA FIXED.

Calvin and Hobbes

by WATTERSON

I FEEL A BIG SNEEZE WELLING UP.

...WHICH IS ALWAYS A SURE SIGN THAT I'M NOT CARRYING A HANDKERCHIEF.

AH... AH... AH..

CHOOOOO!

MOM, I SNEEZED AND BLEW MY HEAD OFF!

PULL YOUR SHIRT DOWN, CALVIN. YOU'RE NOT FOOLING ANYONE.

MOM WOULD BE A LOT MORE FUN IF SHE WAS A LITTLE MORE GULLIBLE.

WATTERSON

Calvin and Hobbes

by WATTERSON

IF *I* WAS IN CHARGE, WE'D NEVER SEE GRASS BETWEEN OCTOBER AND MAY.

ON "THREE," READY? ONE... TWO... THREE!

SNOW!

I SAID SNOW! C'MON! SNOW!

SNOW!

OK THEN, *DON'T* SNOW! SEE WHAT *I* CARE! I *LIKE* THIS WEATHER! LET'S HAVE IT FOREVER!

PLEEAASE SNOW! PLEASE?? JUST A FOOT! OK, EIGHT INCHES! THAT'S ALL! C'MON! SIX INCHES, EVEN! HOW ABOUT JUST SIX??

I'M *WAAIIITING...*

RRRRGGH4H

DO YOU WANT ME TO BECOME AN ATHEIST?

Calvin and Hobbes

by WATTERSON

AHH... THE PERFECT SLUSHBALL!

HARD ENOUGH TO STING, YET SLOPPY ENOUGH TO DRIBBLE DOWN THE COLLAR AND SOAK THE UNDERGARMENTS.

HERE COMES SUSIE! NOW'S MY CHANCE TO HIT HER WITH A SLUSHBALL!

I SEE YOU! YOU'D BETTER NOT THROW THAT! SANTA CLAUS IS WATCHING YOU RIGHT NOW!

ZINGG

FWISSHHH!

WHAP!

OH YES! YES! IT WAS WORTH IT! WHAT A SHOT! I'M NOT SORRY! OH, IT WAS BEAUTIFUL! I'D DO IT AGAIN IN A MINUTE! HA HA!

SANTA'S GONNA SKIP THIS BLOCK FOR YEARS.

94

Calvin and Hobbes

by WATTERSON

WELL, IT'S A NEW YEAR.

AND I'D SAY THE FIRST 10 HOURS HAVEN'T BEEN UP TO SNUFF.

DID YOU MAKE ANY NEW YEAR'S RESOLUTIONS?

YOU BET! I RESOLVED TO QUIT HIDING MY FEELINGS SO MUCH! FROM NOW ON, THE WORLD'S GONNA KNOW EXACTLY WHAT I THINK OF IT!

YES, YOU'VE CERTAINLY BEEN THE MODEL OF SELF-RESTRAINT AND UNDER-STATEMENT UP UNTIL NOW.

WELL NO MORE.

AND I'VE *ALSO* RESOLVED NOT TO PUT UP WITH SARCASTIC TIGERS.

IF I SEE ANY, I'LL TELL THEM.

WATTERSON

Calvin and Hobbes
by WATTERSON

OK, LET'S SEE... IF THE WIND IS BLOWING NORTH-NORTHEAST AT 6 MPH, AND I THROW THE SNOWBALL DUE WEST AT 90 MPH WITH A SLIGHT TOP SPIN....

HA! SUSIE DIDN'T EVEN HEAR ME SNEAK UP!

NOW I'LL CREAM HER CRANIUM WITH A BARRAGE OF SNOWBALLS!

WHIZZZ

PIFF

PIFF

THESE DARN CROSS BREEZES! SHE DIDN'T EVEN NOTICE!

YOU'RE THE WORST SHOT IN THE WORLD, CALVIN! IF IT WASN'T FOR GRAVITY, YOU PROBABLY COULDN'T EVEN HIT THE GROUND!

SMACK!

I DID IT! I DID IT! JUST WHEN IT REALLY COUNTED, I DID IT! HA HA HA! RIGHT IN THE KISSER! HA HA!

BAD NEWS, MOM. I PROMISED MY SOUL TO THE DEVIL THIS AFTERNOON.

OH? THAT RECENTLY?

Calvin and Hobbes
by WATTERSON

THE VALIANT SPACEMAN SPIFF IS LED BY HIS CAPTORS TO A SECRET DUNGEON TO BE DEBRIEFED!

LITTLE DO THEY REALIZE THAT OUR HERO DOESN'T *WEAR* BRIEFS!

EAT YOUR DINNER, CALVIN.

UGH.

POISED PRECARIOUSLY OVER A PERCOLATING PIT OF PUTRID PASTA, SPACEMAN SPIFF IS HELD PRISONER!

STILL WON'T TALK, EH, EARTHLING?

OUR HERO'S MIND RACES FURIOUSLY!

HE'S HAD HIS CHANCE! LET'S MAKE HIM EAT!

LOOK BEHIND YOU!!

KAPWINNGG!

FOOL! THE HUMAN SCUM ESCAPED!

NOT FOR LONG, ZOKBAR-2! AND TOMORROW MORNING HE'LL HAVE COLD MANICOTTI FOR BREAKFAST!

Calvin and Hobbes

by WATTERSON

CALVIN and HOBBES by WATTERSON

CLUMP

THE PTERANODON SPREADS HIS GIANT WINGS, AND..

Calvin and Hobbes by WATTERSON

> I CAN NEVER ENJOY SUNDAYS, BECAUSE IN THE BACK OF MY MIND I ALWAYS KNOW I'VE GOT TO GO TO SCHOOL THE NEXT DAY.

> IT'S LIKE TRYING TO ENJOY YOUR LAST MEAL BEFORE THE EXECUTION.

> A PENNY FOR YOUR THOUGHTS.

> SORRY. *MY* THOUGHTS ARE A BUCK APIECE.

> A DOLLAR?! THAT'S OUTRAGEOUS! YOUR THOUGHTS AREN'T WORTH THAT!

> *THIS* ONE IS! AT A DOLLAR, IT'S THE BARGAIN OF A LIFETIME.

> I WOULDN'T PAY A NICKLE FOR ANY THOUGHT YOU'VE EVER HAD IN YOUR WHOLE FLEA-RIDDEN EXISTENCE!

> THAT LITTLE REMARK JUST MADE THE PRICE *TEN* DOLLARS!

> *TEN??* YOU CAN'T EXTORT ME! *KEEP* YOUR STUPID THOUGHT!

> IF YOU KNEW WHAT IT WAS, YOU'D *BEG* TO PAY TEN BUCKS FOR IT.

> C'MON, JUST TELL ME WHAT IT IS, WILL YOU?

> NOTHING DOING, PAL.

> OK, OK! I'LL GIVE YOU 25 CENTS. THAT'S ALL I HAVE.

> LET'S SEE IT.

> *HERE!* 25 CENTS! NOW WHAT'S THIS BIG, EXPENSIVE THOUGHT OF YOURS?!

> "A FOOL AND HIS MONEY ARE SOON PAR...."

WATTERSON

CALVIN AND HOBBES

by WATTERSON

SIGHHHHHH..

WHAP

SIGHHHHHH..

CALVIN and HOBBES

by WATTERSON

GET UP, CALVIN! I'M NOT GOING TO CALL YOU AGAIN!

I BET.
° ° °

YOU'RE GOING TO MISS THE BUS! NOW GET OUT OF BED!

YOU DON'T KNOW THE ANSWER? THEN SIT DOWN.

Hey, Twinky, want to see if there's an afterlife?

NO, YOU CAN'T GO PLAY UNTIL YOU FINISH YOUR HOMEWORK.

JUST EAT YOUR FOOD. YOU DON'T NEED TO PLAY WITH IT.

STOP STALLING AND GET IN THE BATHTUB.

NO, YOU CAN'T STAY UP A LITTLE LONGER. GO TO BED.

HAVE A GOOD NIGHT'S SLEEP. TOMORROW'S ANOTHER BIG DAY!

... SIGHHHHHH ...

Calvin and Hobbes

by WATTERSON

THREE... TWO... ONE...

LIGHT SPEED!

BLASTING ACROSS THE GALAXY IN HYPER LIGHT DRIVE, IT'S *SPACEMAN SPIFF*, INTERPLANETARY EXPLORER EXTRAORDIN...

SINCE CALVIN SEEMS TO BE ENJOYING THE LESSON, LET'S HAVE HIM DEMONSTRATE THE NEXT PROBLEM.

ZOUNDS! A ZOK DEATH SLOOP APPEARS OUT OF NOWHERE AND FRIES SPIFF'S STABILIZERS!

OUR HERO HURLS OUT OF CONTROL TOWARD HIS IMMINENT DOOM!

11
- 3

THE SITUATION IS DESPERATE! THIS COULD BE THE END! WHAT CAN OUR HERO DO??

HIS MIND RACING FURIOUSLY, SPIFF SPRINGS INTO ACTION! HE DOWNSHIFTS HIS SPACECRAFT AND...

... STALLS.

RINGG!

OH, DARN, OUT OF TIME.

ONCE AGAIN SPACEMAN SPIFF BEATS ALL ODDS TO SAVE THE DAY!

Calvin and Hobbes

by WATTERSON

I'M HOME!

YAHHH!

SLAM!

WHAT A CHUMP!

KNOCK KNOCK

FORGET IT, YOU MORON! I'M NOT OPENING THE DOOR! YOU CAN JUST STAY OUT THERE ALL NIGHT!

OH, I CAN'T *WAIT* TO HEAR *THIS* ONE EXPLAINED.

CalviN and HobbEs

by WATTERSON

I CAN'T SLEEP.

I THINK NIGHTTIME IS DARK SO YOU CAN IMAGINE YOUR FEARS WITH LESS DISTRACTION.

AT NIGHTTIME, THE WORLD ALWAYS SEEMS SO BIG AND SCARY, AND I ALWAYS SEEM SO SMALL.

I WISH I COULD FALL ASLEEP, SO IT WOULD BE MORNING.

SIGHHHHH..

LOOK AT HOBBES. *HE'S* ASLEEP.

Z

HEH HEH... HE SURE LOOKS FUNNY WHEN HE SLEEPS. TIGERS CLOSE THEIR EYES SO TIGHT. I WONDER WHAT HE'S DREAMING ABOUT.

GOOD OL' HOBBES. WHAT A FRIEND.

Z

THINGS ARE NEVER QUITE AS SCARY WHEN YOU'VE GOT A BEST FRIEND.

Z

Z

Z   Z

WATTERSON

Calvin and Hobbes
by WATTERSON

TRUE FRIENDS ARE HARD TO COME BY.

I NEED MORE MONEY.

I WISH PEOPLE WERE MORE LIKE ANIMALS.

ANIMALS DON'T TRY TO CHANGE YOU OR MAKE YOU FIT IN. THEY JUST ENJOY THE PLEASURE OF YOUR COMPANY.

ANIMALS AREN'T CONDITIONAL ABOUT FRIENDSHIPS. ANIMALS LIKE YOU JUST THE WAY YOU ARE.

THEY LISTEN TO YOUR PROBLEMS, THEY COMFORT YOU WHEN YOU'RE SAD, AND ALL THEY ASK IN RETURN IS A LITTLE KINDNESS.

WHOOONK! *SOB* IT'S SO...SO *TRUE!* HOOOOT! THBPBTPTH!

...AND SPEAKING OF "A LITTLE KINDNESS," I'D HAVE A TUNA FISH SANDWICH ANY TIME SOON THAT YOU HAPPEN TO MAKE ONE...

OF COURSE, *SOME* ANIMALS GET ON YOUR NERVES ONCE IN A WHILE.

Calvin and Hobbes

by WATTERSON

MILD-MANNERED CALVIN IS STUCK INSIDE DOING MATH PROBLEMS ON A BEAUTIFUL SUNDAY.

NO ONE IS WATCHING! HE DASHES INTO HIS CLOSET! **THIS** IS A JOB FOR...

STUPENDOUS MAN!

DEFENDER OF FREEDOM! ADVOCATE OF LIBERTY!

A BRIGHT CRIMSON STREAK BLASTS UP THROUGH THE ATMOSPHERE, AND THEN TURNS BACK TOWARD EARTH!

GAINING STUPENDOUS MOMENTUM, *STUPENDOUS MAN* STRIKES THE GROUND AT AN ACUTE ANGLE WITH STUPENDOUS FORCE!

THE EARTH SLOWLY STOPS ROTATING... AND BEGINS TO TURN IN THE OPPOSITE DIRECTION!

PUSHING WITH ALL HIS MIGHT, *STUPENDOUS MAN* TURNS THE PLANET ALL THE WAY AROUND BACKWARD! THE SUN SETS IN THE EAST AND RISES IN THE WEST! SOON IT'S 10 A.M. THE PREVIOUS DAY!

WHAT ARE YOU DOING OUTSIDE? DID YOU FINISH YOUR HOMEWORK ALREADY?

IT'S SATURDAY! I DON'T NEED TO DO IT UNTIL TOMORROW... THANKS TO *STUPENDOUS MAN!*

Calvin and Hobbes

by WATTERSON

DEAR MOM,
HOW DO I LOVE YOU?
LET ME COUNT THE WAYS:

ONE.... NUMBER ONE .....HMM... NUMMMBER ONE .... MM.....

HEY, MOM, WAKE UP! I MADE YOU A MOTHER'S DAY CARD!

WHY, HOW SWEET OF YOU!

I DID IT ALL BY MYSELF. GO AHEAD AND READ IT!

"I WAS GOING TO BUY A CARD WITH HEARTS OF PINK AND RED, BUT THEN I THOUGHT I'D RATHER SPEND THE MONEY ON ME, INSTEAD."

"IT'S AWFULLY HARD TO BUY THINGS WHEN ONE'S ALLOWANCE IS SO SMALL...

..AHEM..

...SO I GUESS YOU'RE PRETTY LUCKY I GOT YOU ANYTHING AT ALL."

"HAPPY MOTHER'S DAY TO YOU. THERE, I SAID IT. NOW I'M DONE. SO HOW 'BOUT GETTING OUT OF BED, AND COOKING BREAKFAST FOR YOUR SON?"

I'M DEEPLY MOVED.

DID YOU NOTICE THE PART ABOUT MY ALLOWANCE?

CALVIN and HOBBES

by WATTERSON

AHHHH...

UH-OH. SOMETHING IS SERIOUSLY WRONG HERE.

THE LAWS OF PERSPECTIVE HAVE BEEN REPEALED!

OBJECTS NO LONGER DIMINISH IN SIZE WITH DISTANCE!

LINES DO NOT CONVERGE TOWARD ANY POINT ON THE HORIZON!

ALL SPATIAL RELATIONSHIPS ARE LOST! IT'S IMPOSSIBLE TO JUDGE WHERE ANYTHING IS! OH NO!

CALVIN, QUIT RUNNING AROUND AND CRASHING INTO THINGS, OR I'LL SELL YOU TO THE MONKEY HOUSE!

...AND NOW *SHE'S* LOST PERSPECTIVE.

Calvin and Hobbes

by WATTERSON

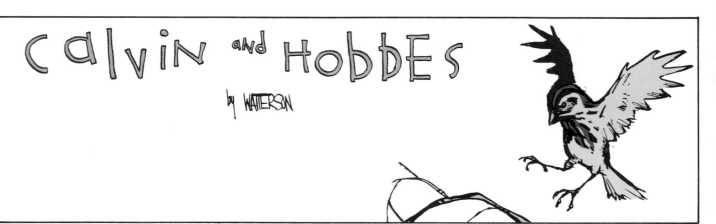

CALVIN and HOBBES

by WATTERSON

DO RE MI FA SO LA TI DO

A SPARROW ALIGHTS UPON A TREE BRANCH.

BUT THIS IS NO *ORDINARY* SPARROW! THIS IS A *SONG* SPARROW!

SWAYING GENTLY IN THE BREEZE, HE PREPARES TO BURST FORTH IN RAPTUROUS MELODY!

ON TOP OF SPA- GHETTI

ALL COVERED WITH CHEEEESE, I LOST MY POOR MEEEATBALLL, WHEN...

WATTERSON

YOU'RE OUT!

DOINK!

I THINK THE BASES ARE TOO DARN FAR APART.

AHH, YOU'RE JUST A BIG SISSY.

CALVIN and HOBBES

by WATTERSON

CLICK

UH OH...

THE SKY IS A DEEP ORANGE! CALVIN'S SKIN IS A PALE GREEN! YELLOW FLOWERS ARE NOW BLUE!

EVERY COLOR IS THE OPPOSITE OF WHAT IT SHOULD BE!

CALVIN HAS BEEN TRANSFERRED TO A COLOR FILM NEGATIVE!

HIS ONLY HOPE IS TO BE PROCESSED BY A 1-HOUR PHOTO FINISHER! DEVELOPER! I NEED DEVELOPER!

DOGGONE IT, CALVIN! THAT'S *ANOTHER* PICTURE RUINED! CAN'T YOU LOOK PLEASANT FOR 1/500TH OF A SECOND?!

DARLINGGG, I'M HOME! ..AND I BROUGHT A SURPRISE!

LET'S HOPE IT'S A DIVORCE!

DARLING, I STOPPED AT THE HOSPITAL ON THE WAY HOME FROM WORK.

DON'T CALL ME "DARLING," OK?

I BROUGHT HOME OUR NEW BABY!

A *BABY*?! I DON'T WANT A BABY!

WHAT SHALL WE NAME HIM?

OUR BABY IS A *RABBIT*?!? HOW COME WE HAVE A RABBIT?!

HE'S *NOT* A RABBIT, HE'S A LITTLE BOY! WE'LL CALL HIM "JEFFREY," OK?

HE LOOKS LIKE A RABBIT TO *ME*.

WELL, JUST **PRETEND** HE'S A BABY!

NO! THIS IS IDIOTIC! I REFUSE!!

PLAYING "HOUSE" MAKES ME SICK! I'M LEAVING!

I DON'T SEE WHY YOU'LL PLAY PRETEND WITH YOUR DUMB OL' TIGER, BUT NOT WITH MR. BUN!

calvin and hobbes
by WATTERSON

FWOOSH

HEH HEH HEH...

YOU'RE IN TROUBLE *NOW*, HOBBES! HEH HEH HEH!

WHILE YOU HAVE JUST *ONE* WATER BALLOON, I HAVE *THREE!* I'M A WALKING ARSENAL OF HYDRO-WEAPONRY!

HA HA! I CAN SEE THE FEAR IN YOUR EYES! YOU REALIZE THAT I CAN GET YOU THREE TIMES WETTER THAN YOU CAN GET ME!

THROW YOUR BALLOON, AND YOUR UTTER SOGGINESS IS ASSURED! *I*, ON THE OTHER HAND, CAN ACT WITH IMPUNITY! WITH THREE BALLOONS, I FEAR NOTHING!

CATCH.

HEY! DON'T! MY ARMS ARE FULL!

OH NO!

SPLOOSH GISSHH SPLASH FWOOSH

WE SUPER-POWERS HAVE IT TOUGH.

MAYBE YOU SHOULD STOCK UP ON BRAINS INSTEAD!

AFTERWORD

Long ago the Sunday comics were printed the size of an entire newspaper page. Each comic was like a color poster. Not surprisingly, with all that space to fill, cartoonists produced works of incredible beauty and power that we just don't see anymore, now that strips are a third or a quarter of their former size. Whereas Little Nemo could dream through 15 surreal panels back in the early part of the century, today it's rare to see a Sunday strip with more than six panels—especially if the characters move. All the things that make comics fun to read—the stories, the dialogue, the pictures—have gotten simpler and simpler in order to keep the work legible at smaller and smaller sizes. The art form has been in a process of retrograde evolution for decades. For those of us trying to return some of the childhood fun we had marveling at comic drawings, the opportunities today are discouraging.

Cartoons can be much more than we've been seeing lately. How much more will depend on what newspaper readers will demand. One thing, though, is certain: little boys, like tigers, will roam all the territory they can get.

—BILL WATTERSON

The End